The Very Frustrated Monster

a WorryWoo tale

by Andi Green

ISBN 978-0-9914952-2-1
Printed in the USA

To see all The WorryWoo Monsters®
go to www.WorryWoos.com

This book is dedicated to you.

Have you ever had a day

when nothing goes right,

and you wonder

"why me"

from morning

to night?

Well, a monster named

Twitch

was having that day—

everything around him
  seemed to go the *wrong* way!

It started at sunrise…
his alarm didn't ring,
and thus began a day filled with
frustrating things.

He *stubbed* his two toes as he jumped out of bed,

tripped on his backpack

and *bumped* his horned head!

For breakfast Twitch wanted wheat toast and Woo tea

but the bread was all *gone...*

how could this be?

So he left without eating, **locked** his keys in the house...

Twitch became quite *upset* and he made a big *fuss,*

to add to his *troubles—*

he was late for his bus!

Though he ran very fast
to get to the stop,
his ride passed him by...
Twitch was ready to

POP!

To calm himself down,
    Twitch counted to **ten;**
        he took **four** deep breaths...
            and began once again.

Twitch walked into school
filled to the brim
with all of the feelings
that were *bothering* him.

An emotional volcano *bubbled* within;

the *preSSUre* Twitch felt

seemed to make his world spin!

The grass was *too* green…

the sun was *too* bright,

his lunch tasted *funny*...

his gym shorts were *tight*!

Twitch froze up on stage
and the words
came out
wrong.

When handed a prize,
Twitch became very *flushed*.
It wasn't first place—
now his spirits were *crushed!*

Twitch *bristled* and *brewed* and let

frustration win!

He *threw* down his ribbon
and *yelled* at his peers;

Twitch was so *overwhelmed* that he broke into tears.

His friends scurried off
as fast as they could

'cause a *frustrated* Twitch
was *never* good!

as he looked all around
to find someone to *blame.*

But alone Twitch did stand—
there was nobody else.

His *monstrous* ways
had left him all by himself.

Then he noticed a squirrel running up a big tree.

It was carrying acorns

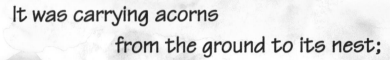

from the ground to its nest;

when some fell

d
  o
    w
      n,

it went back
for the rest.

And the nuts that were *cracked*
or *scattered* from the fall

didn't stop the small squirrel...

didn't stop it at all.

The squirrel may have been **flustered** when things went awry.

but it brushed itself off and
continued to try.

For this bushy-tailed creature
knew it couldn't control
the *wind*

And the harder it worked,
the more Twitch could see

that life's little

frustrations

are what you make

them to be.

You can let them *upset* you

and *spoil* your day…

or you can turn
things around in a
positive way!

The following morning

Twitch woke up on time

He showed off his ribbon,
as *proud* as could be...

then hung it from a branch...
on the squirrel's
favorite tree!

the
end

FRUSTRATION JOURNAL

I feel frustrated because...

When I get frustrated I feel...

Next time I feel frustrated I will...

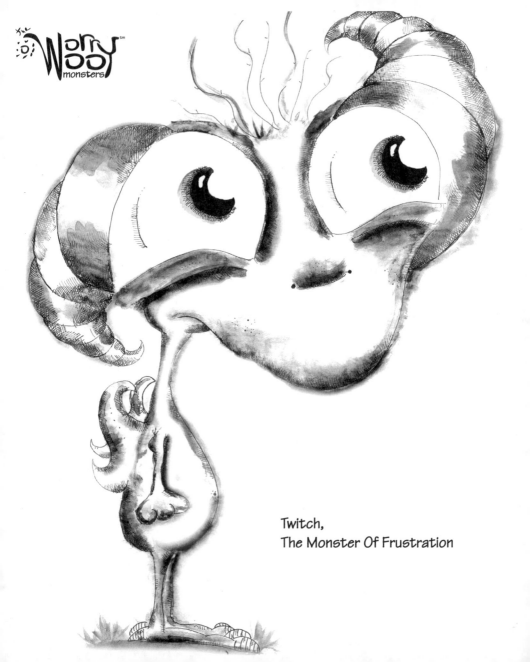

Twitch,
The Monster Of Frustration

Draw Your Own
Frustration Monster

More WorryWoo Books

Don't Feed The WorryBug
Say hello to Wince, one of the biggest worriers you will every meet. From cookies to homework to the weather, Wince worries about everything. And when Wince starts to worry, his WorryBug appears. At first the WorryBug is small and non-threatening, but the more Wince worries the more his WorryBug grows. Join Wince as he discovers the secret to keeping his worries from getting monstrous. Using unique drawings and clever rhymes, Don't Feed The WorryBug carries an insightful message that readers of all ages will enjoy.

2019 Child Mind Institute Pick - "Best Books About Mental Health"

The Monster Who Wanted It All
Zelly, The Monster of Envy, wants EVERYTHING… especially if it belongs to someone else! From his clothes to his toys, he's never content with what he has. His demanding "Mine, Mine, Mine" attitude is affecting everyone around him and turning him green with envy. If only he could be a king—then he'd have it all… or would he? Follow Zelly on a personal journey that teaches him about expectations and, ultimately, appreciation.

The Monster in The Bubble
Squeek, is afraid to try new things. He hides in his cozy bubble planning all the things he would do if he just took that big step. He dreams of meeting new friends, climbing huge mountains and even flying to the moon. But every time he thinks about leaving, he decides it is better to stay. Will Squeek ever leave? Sometimes you need that push from your Bubble to show you how great the world really is. A heartwarming story for children & adults of all ages.

The Monster Who Couldn't Decide

Should I do this or should I do that? Do I go here or do I go there? From pancakes to hats to flying a kite, Fuddle, The Monster of Confusion, cant decide what's just right! Through the use of humorous rhymes and illustrations, creator Andi Green, guides readers through the world of a monster who cant make up her mind. The Monster Who Couldn't Decide, the fourth story from the award winning WorryWoos series, is an amusing empathetic story that all readers can relate to.

The Nose That Didn't Fit

Rue, The Monster of Insecurity, feels that his nose doesn't fit and spends most of his time hoping that it would shrink quite a bit. From wearing nose cover ups to doing balancing tricks, he attempts to find ways to deal with what he feels is a very BIG problem. Follow Rue as he struggles with self acceptance and learns that beauty is truly in the eye of the beholder.

The Lonely Little Monster

Nola has a problem... she doesn't have any friends. Join The Lonely Little Monster on an imaginative tale which deals with the importance of seeing the world in a different way. Through the use of whimsical illustrations, we follow the main character as she ponders her plight. The heartwarming ending puts a positive spin on a common situation and proves that things can change, especially if you open your eyes!

WorryWoos.com